W. S. GILBERT'S

THE DUKE
OF PLAZA TORO

From The Gondoliers *by W. S. Gilbert and Arthur Sullivan*

Set to Pictures by *L. L.*

ROSEMARY WELLS

THE MACMILLAN COMPANY, NEW YORK
COLLIER-MACMILLAN LIMITED, LONDON

Text adapted from the song "In Enterprise of Martial Kind"
from *The Gondoliers or The King of Barataria*
by W. S. Gilbert and Arthur Sullivan

The Macmillan Company, New York
Collier-Macmillan Canada, Ltd., Toronto, Ontario
Library of Congress catalog card number: 69-10499
Printed in the United States of America

FIRST PRINTING

For T. Wells

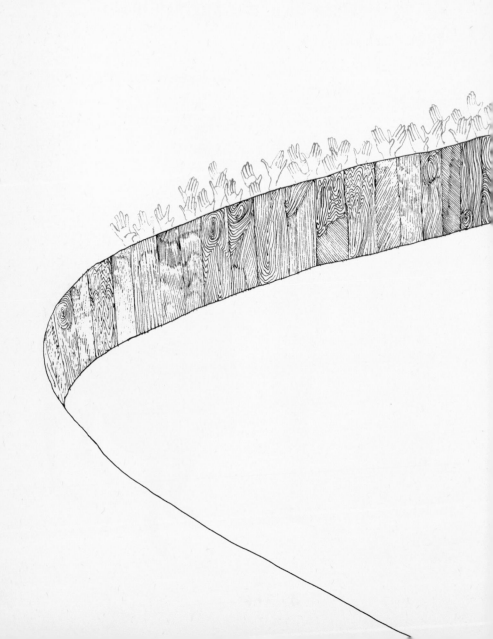

In enterprise of martial kind
When there was any fighting,

He led his regiment from behind—
He found it less exciting.

But when away his regiment ran
His place was at the fore, O!

That celebrated
cultivated
underrated nobleman
The Duke of Plaza Toro.

When to evade destruction's hand,
To hide they all proceeded,

No soldier in that gallant band
Hid half as well as he did.

He lay concealed
throughout the war,
And so preserved
his gore, O!

That undetected
unaffected
well-connected
warrior
The Duke of Plaza Toro.

LASELL JUNIOR COLLEGE

When told that they would all be shot
Unless they left the service,

Our hero hesitated not,
So marvelous his nerve is.
He sent his resignation in,
The first of all his corps, O!

LASELL JUNIOR COLLEGE

That very knowing
overflowing
easy-going paladin...

The Duke of Plaza Toro.

To men of grosser clay
He always showed the way,

That very knowing
overflowing
easy-going paladin
The Duke of Plaza Toro.

"In Enterprise of Martial Kind"

Lyrics by W. S. Gilbert   Music by Arthur Sullivan

In— en - ter - prise of mar - tial kind, When

there was an - y— fight - ing, He— led his regi - ment

from be - hind, He found it less— ex - cit - ing. But—

when a - way his regi - ment ran, His place was— at the

fore, O! That cel - e - brat - ed, cul - ti - vat - ed,

un - der - rat - ed no - ble - man, The Duke of Pla - za—

To - ro! In the first and fore - most flight, ha, ha! You

To - ro! In— ev - 'ry dough - ty deed, ha, ha! He

al - ways took the lead, ha, ha! That

un - af - fect - ed, un - de - tect - ed, well - con - nect - ed war - ri - or, The

Duke— of— Pla - za To - ro!

When— told that they would all be shot Un -

less they left— the— serv - ice, That— he - ro hes - i -

tat - ed not, So mar - vel - ous— his— nerve is. He—

sent his res - ig - na - tion in, The first of— all his

corps, O! That ver - y know - ing, o - ver - flow - ing,

eas - y - go - ing pal - a - din, The Duke of Pla - za—

To - ro! To— men of gross - er clay, ha, ha! He

al - ways showed the way, ha, ha! That

ver - y know-ing, o - ver -flow-ing, eas - y - go - ing pal - a - din, The

Duke— of— Pla - za To - ro! That

ver - y know-ing, o - ver -flow-ing, eas - y - go - ing pal - a - din, The

Duke— of— Pla - za To - ro!